Also by Adeline Foo

⭐ **THE DIARY OF AMOS LEE**
I Sit, I Write, I Flush!

⭐ **THE DIARY OF AMOS LEE**
Girls, Guts and Glory!

⭐ **THE DIARY OF AMOS LEE**
I'm Twelve, I'm Tough, I Tweet!

Find out more at
www.amoslee.com.sg

Whoopie Lee
almost famous

Written by
adeline foo

Illustra
STEPHAN

EPIGRAM BOOKS/SINGAPORE

SECOND PRINTING, 2011

Text © Adeline Foo 2011

Illustrations © Epigram 2011

PUBLISHED BY EPIGRAM

1008 Toa Payoh North #03-08

Singapore 318996

Tel: (65) 6292 4456

enquiry@epigram.com.sg

www.epigram.com.sg

**ILLUSTRATIONS AND
COVER DESIGN BY**

Stephanie Wong

**NATIONAL LIBRARY BOARD SINGAPORE
CATALOGUING IN PUBLICATION DATA**

Foo, Adeline, 1971–

Whoopie Lee: Almost Famous/Adeline Foo;

Illustrated by Stephanie Wong. – Singapore: Epigram, 2011.

p. cm.

ISBN: 978-981-08-8413-0 (pbk.)

1. Girls – Singapore – Juvenile fiction. 2. Fame – Juvenile fiction.
I. Wong, Stephanie, 1979–II. Title.

PZ7

S823 – dc22   OCN712624548

Printed in Singapore

I'm nine. I'm a middle child. My mother named me Whoopie. What can be worse than that? What is a Whoopie anyway? If you Google it, you will find Whoopi Goldberg, the American actress, the Whoopee cushion and the Whoopie pie.

No, my name wasn't inspired by any of the movies that my mother had seen Whoopi Goldberg in. Neither was it induced by the fart sound produced by the Whoopee cushion when you sit on it.

Yes, that's right, my name was inspired by the Whoopie pie! My mother ate her first Whoopie pie when she was pregnant with me. And the name stuck. If you think that's weird, wait till you hear what my older brother is called. He's named Amos, after the cookies! My kid brother is named after a mountain: Everest!

Being a middle child is tough. It means you're the last to get noticed. Amos always gets what he wants because he is the oldest. He gets to choose the first chocolate in the box, and if there's only one Oreo doughnut in a box of six, he will get it, because he's the Big Brother. As for Everest, the youngest, he gets all the attention in the family. When Dad or Mum comes home, the first thing they ask is, "Where's the baby?" or "Ooh-coochie-coochie-coo… how's baby today?" No one remembers to ask about me.

When I was younger, I had to whine to get my way. Amos coined the acronym WPI from Whoopie. Amos says it stands for "Witty, Pretty and Intelligent". But I know he's lying. I've read his diary. He meant it to be "Whiny, Pesky and Irritating".

Once, I told Dad I'd like to change my name. He just laughed and said I have the sweetest name in the world. "Whoopie, the Big Oreo Pie. You're the sweet, creamy vanilla frosting!" That's the nicest thing anyone has said about my name.

I am the middle child stuck between two brothers.
I am the centre — the sticky part that holds the two pies
together. I guess Dad's right; my brothers would be plain
boring without me. They had better not forget that!

Guess I'm stuck with it. Whoopie Lee, that's my name.
Whiny, Pesky and Irritating? Never! I'm going to prove
that I'm better than Amos. The Whoopie pie definitely
tastes better than a Famous Amos cookie.

One day, I will be even more famous than my brother.
My quest for fame begins now.

a new Beginning

Amos, at thirteen, is in secondary school. He didn't make it to Raffles Institution after his PSLE. Raffles Institution is one of the oldest and most prestigious schools in Singapore. It is named after Sir Stamford Raffles who founded Singapore in 1819. I know Mum cried when she realised that Amos was nowhere near the cut-off mark to get into Raffles Institution.

Really, what was she thinking?

I knew that he wouldn't make it! He had been spending too much time on computer games and shooting stupid pigs with angry birds on his iPhone. Besides, he's just not smart enough.

Hasn't mum heard the saying before? There's always a black sheep in the family. In ours, there are two. The cookie and the mountain. As for me? I'm the shepherd. I'm always the one who has to look out for my brothers, like getting Amos' school uniform ironed, his tube of toothpaste replaced when it's finished or top up Everest's drawer of pull-up pants when they're out. But I know my brothers will never admit I'm important.

Anyway, over dinner last night, Mum suddenly asked me if I wanted to write a book. A book! She said I could

start by recording events in my life, in the form of weekly chapters. Hmmm… I like that. Only important people keep diaries, right? I know Amos became very famous in school because of his toilet diary. He even created "Poop Fiction" for the school magazine, gaining a huge following on Twitter. I wonder if that will make me famous, carrying on his legacy?

But I'm **DEFINITELY NOT** writing in the toilet. Yes, my brother does a lot of writing in the toilet. He says he can only find his creative spark when doing his big business.

Let's see how this sounds…

The Diary of Whoopie Lee

Better than the Diary of Amos Lee!

Guaranteed to keep you longer in the toilet.

I love it.

Mum, I know you're reading this. I've looked up the words in the dictionary.

FROM THE DICTIONARY
★ **Acronym**: *[ak-ruh-nim]*
  A word formed from the initial letters of other words.
  (Oh I get it, like KISS – Keep It Simple, Stupid!)

  Legacy: *[leg-uh-see]*
  Something that is passed on.

That's good! And no, I did NOT cry when Amos failed to get into Raffles Institution, my eyes were tearing from frying eggs and onions.

Some things just never change.
Mum used to read Amos' diary too.

THE DIARY OF WHOOPIE LEE

Mum calls this the biography section.
(The dictionary says it's a description of a person's life.)

ABOUT ME

HEIGHT: 1.3 m
WEIGHT: 25 kg
HAIR: Long
COLOUR: Black

WHAT I LOVE TO DO:
Reading and watching television.

FAVOURITE BOOKS:
Junie B. Jones by Barbara Park, St. Clare's by Enid Blyton,
Science Encyclopaedia, The Dictionary.

FAVOURITE TV SHOWS:
Hannah Montana, Fighting Spiders.

FAVOURITE CARTOONS:
Winx Club, SpongeBob SquarePants, Mr. Bean and
Go, Diego, Go (only because I have to babysit Everest).

FAVOURITE MOVIES:

Despicable Me, Megamind, all the Shrek movies!
And of course, Toy Story too.

FAVOURITE HOBBIES:

Collecting Pokemon cards (the ones Amos doesn't want),
drawing, singing, thinking of ways to be famous!

FAVOURITE FOODS:

1   **The French Macaron –** Made with egg whites, icing
sugar, sugar and ground almonds. The English call it
a macaroon; the French call it a macaron. It looks like
mini "burgers" with buttercream or jam sandwiched
in between. When you bite into it, it's so light that it
simply melts in your mouth! Ummm...

2   **The Japanese Dorayaki –** Two small pancakes
sandwiched with a filling of red bean paste. It's really
soft and sponge-like. I eat it for breakfast and supper!

3   **The Ming Jiang Kueh –** A local peanut-filled
pancake! It's sold at coffeeshops and wet markets,
made fresh on the spot. When cooked, ground
peanuts and sugar are spread over the pancake, then
it's folded in half and cut into slices. Other types of
fillings include peanut butter and red bean paste.

(See, every culture has a Whoopie pie. It just comes in a different form. And remember this — the centre is always the best part! The sweet, creamy filling.)

FAVOURITE MUSIC:
Baby by Justin Bieber (Ohh wooaah…), Nobody Nobody But You by The Wonder Girls, and Home (the song that the school made us learn for the National Day celebration).

There is a new, awesome remake of Home! I've just heard it on www.thisishome.sg. Check it out!

MY BEST FRIEND:
Morticia Phui. She's in Primary Three like me. I've known her since we were seven! She's really cute and funny. But she's not very bright. It's ok. I can think for two.

MY FAMILY:

Grandpa and Grandma are retirees.

Me, WPI
Witty, Pretty and Intelligent.

Dad works at the airport.

Mum's a blogger.

Everest (The **BIG FAT MOUNTAIN** baby.)

Amos (Who's not too smart. Cookies get eaten, don't they?)

THE Happy TOiLeT project

Our class got involved in a project to make the school toilets user-friendly. My teachers called it the Happy Toilet assignment. I didn't have any idea of what to do, until Amos started calling me a Fart Queen. See, I had been farting really badly. All thanks to Mum's latest craze with onion and garlic. She puts them into everything! So when Amos called me a Fart Queen, I decided to get back at him.

I used Mum's plastic Tupperware box to trap all the gas I released. It took me two hours to make five collections. When Amos was asleep, I released the Tupperware of gas into his bedroom. Too bad my brother's a pig, he slept through all that smell.

I couldn't sleep after what I did, so I stayed up and read all the newspapers in the flat. I came across some funny articles related to poop and I got really excited! I found the answer for my Happy Toilet assignment! Maybe this would make me famous… producing posters for the school toilets! Bet the English teachers will be grateful to me for making kids read. Every minute of reading helps with improving your English, even when bombing.

I asked Mum if she would help me design my posters. She said she was happy to. She created a template for a poster using Microsoft Office Publisher. It was so cool!

Here's a list of what I could do:

1   Poop Art
All about poop-inspired art.

2   Potty Training for Babe
Pigs in Taiwan are being trained to poop in the right places. This will be funny!

3   Gourmet Coffee from the Palm Civet Cat's Poop
Coffee cherries eaten by this cat are collected from its poop and used to prepare one of the world's best coffees.

Ta-da! Am I clever or what? Mum even promised that she would put up my poster on her blog. But when I asked to be paid, she said, "You're nine! Why do you need so much money?" It's so unfair! I know Amos used to get paid when he contributed to her blog. Why can't I get paid?

What's even worse, I got a note from Amos after school. He wrote:

How did he know what I did?

How to Get Back at Older Brothers

If you love anything pink, sleep with a bedtime bear, and brush your teeth every time after a meal, you should seriously skip reading this. But if you have an older brother you want to kill for always getting you into trouble, **MEMORISE THIS ENTIRE ARTICLE!**

Step 1   When you find your brother digging his nose, notice where he discards his pickings. Run a piece of scotch tape over them when he has left the room. Tape the evidence on a piece of paper and note the date they have been picked up. There'll come a day when this gross behaviour of his will come in useful, like when he starts bringing girls to the flat. You can use this and threaten to show his friends! He will do anything that you ask him to.

Step 2   The next time your brother fails to put away his smelly socks, collect them with a pair of disposable gloves. Hide them till night time. Slip the socks into his pillow case just before he gets into bed. When he finds the socks, he would be disgusted beyond words. If he doesn't, you can always remind him to wash his hair before school.

Step 3   Download a photo of a beautiful movie star or a famous model. Someone like Emma Watson (a.k.a. Hermione in Harry Potter) is perfect! Be sure to find a picture where she's wearing a sleeveless dress. Use a fine-tip black marker to draw lots of hair in her underarm. Stick it up beside his bed when he falls asleep at night. You'll be amazed at how loud he can scream when he sees it in the morning.

I showed it to the teacher-in-charge of Happy Toilet, but she told me it was "totally irrelevant". Humph!

HOW TO BE FAMOUS

What is the best way to gain fame? Mum said if I study hard enough and become the top pupil in school, that's the fastest way to become famous. Dad said if I appear on TV, like if I'm being interviewed as the top PSLE student in Singapore, that's a great way to become famous. Really, so unimaginative!

Amos said if I win money in 4D or Toto, I will be famous. I don't trust him. I may be nine but I'm not stupid. I know it's against the law for children to buy lottery!

But, I've figured this out on my own. If I keep an unusual pet, I can be famous!

I have ruled out the usual suspects. Forget dogs, cats, rabbits, guinea pigs or terrapins. I'm thinking of:

1 A Tarantula

2 A Rat, or

3 A Cockroach

You will NOT keep any of these in our flat!

I'm **CRBT**
(Crying Really Big Tears!)

Just use 'sad', please!

You can never win with Mum.

WEEK 03

Becoming a Playwright

I guess I have to find fame another way. Mum suggested I could write a play and have it staged. Wow, I guess that will make me the youngest playwright in Singapore? This sounds like a good idea. Hmmm… maybe I could borrow one of Grandpa's old kampong tales… let's see, what about The Tale of the Headless Chicken?

A Play by Whoopie Lee, the Genius Playwright

SCENE ONE

A forest setting. A fowl, with red-orange feathers and white skinny legs, is pecking at earthworms in the ground. An old man enters the stage.

OLD MAN   Hey, chicken! I'm looking for meat to cook in my wife's stew!

(Red Fowl springs up and cackles in shock.)

RED FOWL   No! You can't eat me! I'm the Guardian of the Ancient Spirit. If you kill me, it would take its revenge on you!

(Red Fowl does a fierce chicken dance to mean business.)

OLD MAN   What is the Ancient Spirit?

RED FOWL   It's a FIERCE animal spirit! It will rip you into pieces! Raarrr!

(Old Man pretends to be scared. He thinks for a bit. He sneaks up behind Red Fowl and grabs it by the neck, strangling it as it screeches madly.)

RED FOWL   Help! Murder!

OLD MAN   Stop that screeching!

(Old Man whips out an axe and chops off Red Fowl's head. It rolls to the ground. The headless Red Fowl runs around for a minute, frightening the old man. Before the old man can react, Red Fowl cackles madly before dashing off stage.)

OLD MAN   What just happened?

(Old Man picks up the head of Red Fowl.)

OLD MAN   The missus will just have to cook with this little piece.

(Old Man exits the stage.)

End of scene.

Casting Call for Actors
– One Old Man & a Chicken

Mum read my play. She said it's funny! She helped me post a casting call for actors on Yahoo! I was so excited when I received eleven replies!

Nine people asked if they needed to put on a chicken suit. I replied immediately. I said I didn't know where to get one. I suggested that they could just stick feathers on their head.

Two e-mails were from volunteers who worked for the Society of Prevention of Cruelty to Animals. They said I was "displaying blatant disregard for animal rights". They said I should be banished to Malaysia to clean out chicken coops. I wrote back and told them I was only nine. Then they replied to say that they would excuse me, but I have to promise not to use a real chicken on stage.

They said that this particular chicken is known as the "red junglefowl" and is an endangered species. I looked up the word in the dictionary. I wrote them back a reply: **"GAL!"**

What does 'GAL' mean?

Get a life.

✦ FROM THE DICTIONARY

Blatant Disregard: *[bleyt-nt] [dis-ri-gahrd]*
Outright or rude lack of attention for something.

Banish: *[ban-ish]*
To be sent away.

Endangered Species: *[en-deyn-jerd] [spee-sheez]*
Group of animals at risk of becoming extinct.
(Like the dinosaurs? Awesome!)

aLL aBOUT HeaDLeSS CreaTUreS

WOW! I got my first fan mail! Someone sent me an article about a chicken that was beheaded in Colorado, USA, back in 1945. This crazy chicken lost its head but could still run around!

Totally true! Scientists who studied the unusual case reported that the chicken's head wasn't completely severed. One ear was left intact, and the chop actually missed the chicken's jugular vein which led to a blood clot that stopped him from bleeding to death.

The chicken's brain stem, which controlled its movements and actions, was unharmed. That explained why the chicken was able to run around "headless"! **AWESOME!**

Cockroach Facts

I looked up the Internet today. Found out that there are more than 5,000 cockroach species in the world! Awesome.

Some scientist even recorded that cockroaches can run at a speed of 5.5km/h, faster than the average walking speed of a human. Double cool!

And this is the best part, like the headless chicken, cockroaches can actually live for up to a week without their heads! So if I kept one for a pet, wouldn't that like make me **VERY FAMOUS?**

If I find a cockroach in this flat, I will ground you! No Hannah Montana and no Winx Club!

Yes, Mum.

GRANDPA & THE RED JUNGLEFOWL

Grandpa told me that there had been several reports of red junglefowls prowling our neighbourhood. People got really excited when they spotted chickens crossing the roads! The birds were even featured in The Straits Times and on many blog sites. It even made news on television!

Mum laughed when Grandpa said he would try to catch one. He even asked if he could have some of her Cordyceps (I think it's the name of a Chinese herb Mum uses in her soups) to feed the chicken.

Really, it's just a silly bird, why get so excited? Anyone would think that Singaporeans are chicken-starved loonies.

And you know what? Amos said I was jealous because even a chicken is more famous than me. I hate Amos!

I'll show him who's really famous. Humph!

THE TALE OF THE HEADLESS CHICKEN AND A PUPPY

I'm adding more scenes to my play. I need more actors. I've asked Morticia, my best friend, if she wanted a part. Sometimes, I wonder if Mum had known Morticia's mum before. Where do these women get the inspiration for their children's names? I've known Morticia since we were seven. She has an older brother who is Amos' classmate – Michael. He's really cute! And sweet to Morticia. Amos hates him. He probably doesn't like him because he looks evil beside Michael.

Morticia and I got closer last year when I recruited her to be my band-mate. It was a period when I was crazy about all things Korean. We were really good! We could sing every single song that the Wonder Girls sang! But we stopped singing when Mum said fame was getting to my head. Whatever that means.

I used to be so popular that many boys were calling me up! But one day, they just stopped. I've always wondered what happened. One boy I knew said there's a monster living in my flat. He said every time he called, he would hear a monster making evil lip-smacking noises. He gave up calling because he was frightened.

Back to Morticia. I've asked her before why her mother named her that. Is she related to the Addams Family or what? She said she didn't know who they were. I never asked her again.

Morticia is a good friend. She's always following me around. So I've decided that she can play a puppy in the play I'm writing. I'm such a good friend too.

A Play by Whoopie Lee, the Genius Playwright
(Part II of The Tale of the Headless Chicken)

SCENE TWO
Old Man's attap hut. Old Man returns home and sees his wife.

OLD MAN   Honey, I'm home! I brought you a chicken!

OLD WOMAN   Great! I'm hungry.

(Old Man throws Red Fowl's head into a pot of boiling water when the Old Woman isn't looking.)

RED FOWL   G-g-g-g-r-r-r-l OUCH!
It's scalding hot! Help! Murder!

OLD WOMAN   Did the chicken just talk?
I heard it screaming in the pot!

OLD MAN   Ignore it! Let it boil to death!

RED FOWL   ARRRGGHHH!!! HELP!
SOMEONE!

(The Old Woman is frightened. She fishes out Red Fowl's head from the pot with a pair of chopsticks and throws it out of the window.)

RED FOWL   At last! Freedom!

(The head of Red Fowl flies through the air, and lands on the ground. A puppy comes running by.)

PUPPY   Yeeeks! What is this ugly creature?

RED FOWL   Who are you calling ugly?

(The puppy is amused with the talking head. It yelps before taking a big bite of it. In one gulp, she swallows it.)

PUPPY   Yoouf!

End of scene.

BROTHERS AND BEST FRIENDS

Found a big word in the dictionary today:
"RHINOTILLEXOMANIA".

It's a term scientists use to describe too much nose-picking.
I think Amos is seriously suffering from this disease. I asked
Amos if I could have his iPhone if he dies from it. And you
know what he did? He shouted for Mum, screaming that
I am cursing him.

Forget about him! Morticia called to say she loved the
part I wrote her in the play. She called me a genius!
See, my best friend is actually smarter than my brother.

She even asked if she could do more in the play.

"Speaking two out of eighteen lines isn't exciting
enough!" she said. I didn't realise she's so hungry
for fame. I thought really hard before I asked if she could
jump through a hoop. She said she could try. I told her
I needed more time to write a longer play with more lines
for her. She promised to wait.

Hmmm… maybe she can play a poodle. That way,
she can also sing, dance and jump through a hoop.
Am I clever or what?

Speaking of animals, I need to get back to designing
my toilet poster. I'm writing about cats next! Meowww…

Gourmet Coffee from a Least Expected Source

Bali, the land of the sun, surf and sea, has a beautiful town called Ubud. Tourists visit Ubud for its food, art, batik, jewellery, ceramics, wood carvings, and… something else, according to travel guide books.

In what is called a kopi luwak plantation, the luwak, a Malay term for palm civet cat, actually eats the coffee berries of the coffee plant. After digestion, the beans of the berries would pass out in the yellow poop of the luwak, which would then be collected, washed, and roasted.

If you haven't freaked out from reading so far, good! The coffee beans are prized for its aroma and rich chocolate taste when brewed as a drink.

The next time your parents visit Bali, tell them to try kopi luwak! But don't bother explaining how this coffee is prepared.

Finally! The Happy Toilet teacher-in-charge said she loved my article! She made copies of the poster and put them up in all the toilets. She even gave me three out of five stars for the effort.

Mum also liked it. She posted it on her blog. But she warned me that she wouldn't be paying me. I can live with that. Fame is more important than money.

HOW TO BE FAMOUS: adopt a cause!

I've figured out that every famous person adopts a cause. Just look at Mr. Bean. He's a funnyman, everybody loves watching him! His cause is to prove that being a loser can also make you famous.

Then there's SpongeBob SquarePants, whose cause is to prove that even if you're an ugly yellow sponge, you can still be famous.

So I've decided that I would adopt a cause! I want to prove that a nine-year-old can do something that no one has thought of. Maybe I can even break a record! Just imagine, the World's Youngest Trainer of a Human Poodle.

THAT'S ME, WHOOPIE LEE.
FAME AT LAST!

Does Morticia know about this?

Yes, Mum. She said she trusts me completely. Honest!

WEEK 06

Training gets real

Grandpa brought home a giant cage today. I was wondering what he needed it for. He said it was a secret. While he was out doing Taiji with Grandma, I borrowed it for an experiment.

I turned the cage on its side and used Dad's screwdriver to remove its door. I carried Everest and placed him inside the cage. He didn't protest. I then rolled the cage and guess what? My baby brother was so smart, he moved along with it!

He was like a hamster running on a spin-wheel! See, I've always known that Everest is a genius, unlike Amos.

Just before Grandpa came home, I screwed the door back on. Pity the cage is too small for Morticia. I have to think of using something else to bring out her poodle instinct.

YOU WILL NOT PUT YOUR BROTHER IN A CAGE AGAIN! HOW COULD YOU!

Oops. Sorry, Mum. I was only conducting an experiment. Promise, I won't do it again. He's too fat to run anyway.

Mum is still mad at me. I offered to wash the dishes, do the laundry, vacuum the floor and iron all our school clothes. Amos asked if I had done something naughty, I told him I'm always Mum's good little helper.

Decided to write another article for Mum's blog to make her happy. She's not so cross with me after I did all the chores. Phew!

Potty Training for Babe

Have you watched Babe, the movie? Did you know that the character of Babe was created by children's book author Dick King-Smith who first wrote it in a book titled The Sheep-Pig? Babe is the story of a runt who rose to fame because of his shepherding ability. Cute!

In an article I read in The Straits Times, farmers in Taiwan were reported to have introduced potty training for pigs! They did this to help curb water and waste pollution.

It began in southern Taiwan where a pig breeder started potty training for 10,000 pigs in late 2009. To keep his animals from passing poop in rivers (which would contaminate drinking water for villagers), the farmer set up special toilets smeared with pigs' urine and faeces to attract the pigs. These pigs were really intelligent! They started using the special piggy toilets, and avoided the rivers. The farmer was then able to reduce the amount of waste pollution by up to 80 percent! This article only proves that animals are intelligent enough to be trained.

Many movies have been made about the intelligence of farm animals. Babe was just one example. There's also Charlotte's Web, a story about the friendship between a pig and a spider. I bet if pigs can be so smart, a poodle would be even cleverer.

This time, I got four out of five stars. I am finally getting some attention in school.

✦ FROM THE DICTIONARY

Runt: *[ruhnt]*
The smallest or weakest animal in a litter.

Pollution: *[puh-loo-shuhn]*
Adding harmful substances into the air or water.

Contaminate: *[kuhn-tam-uh-neyt]*
Make something harmful or unclean.

Shepherding: *[shep-erd-ing]*
To tend or guard over sheep.

WEEK 07
THE TRAINING OF A POODLE

Finally, Grandpa bought me the hula hoop that I asked for! It was really fun twirling it around the waist. Both Morticia and I tried it. She's really good! She could do it for three minutes! I told her to take the hula hoop home. If she trains hard and hits five minutes every time, I'd reward her with a biscuit.

She asked if she could have Famous Amos cookies,
I said no. I told her that they suck! I told her I only eat
Mrs. Field's cookies. She's happy with that.

This afternoon, Grandpa brought home a chicken.
He said it was a wild red junglefowl. Mum was hysterical
when she came home from the market. She saw the
chicken in the cage and screamed so loudly, we thought
she was going to burst a vein.

Grandma said they would cook it after feeding it
Cordyceps for a week. Wow, this sounds like a tale from
Hansel and Gretel. Maybe they can consider popping
Everest into the oven as well. He's been so irritating,
always bugging me to "carry, carry". What's wrong with
his legs? My arms are **ACHING** from carrying him around
all day long!

✦ **FROM THE DICTIONARY**
Hysterical: *[hi-ster-i-kuhl]*
An emotional outburst from fear or grief,
leading to loud weeping or laughter.

grandma's recipe for chicken rice

Talk about being cruel. I heard Grandpa and Grandma discussing different ways of cooking the chicken. The poor chicken squawked every time they yelled, "Chop!" Finally, they decided on steamed chicken rice. Like why is this so special? Can't they just buy a packet from the coffeeshop downstairs?

I told Grandpa he has to be really careful when he chops off the chicken's head. "Don't let it run around headless!" He laughed and said it was a cock-and-bull story. Huh? What does that mean?

Anyway, Grandma said her Hainanese chicken rice recipe is borrowed from the Chinese immigrants who came to Singapore from Hainan, a province in China.

Hmmm... it sounds easy enough to prepare!

How to Cook Hainanese Chicken Rice

Step 1   Clean and dress the chicken
          (with rice wine, salt and pepper).

Step 2   Steam the chicken
          (with ginger, onions and garlic).

Step 3   To prepare the rice, cook it in a rice
          cooker with soup saved from steaming
          the chicken.

Step 4   To eat, chop the chicken into small pieces
          and serve with rice.

Step 5   Drizzle black sauce over the rice
          before eating.

✦ FROM THE DICTIONARY
Immigrant: *[im-i-gruhnt]*
Person from abroad coming into a country to live there.

✦ FROM THE BOOK OF IDIOMS
Cock-and-bull Story – An unbelievable tale.

recipe for the whoopie pie

Talking about food, I found a recipe for the American Whoopie pie on the Internet. Hmmm… we have our own version of the Whoopie pie too! It's called… ta-da, the pancake! Really, all you have to do is to put a filling between two slices of pancakes. It could be peanut butter, cheese, or even durian pulp. I just love desserts. Bet I got my sweet tooth from Mum. Everest should count himself lucky he wasn't named after something sweet, imagine being called Macaron Lee.

Here's My Original
Singapore Whoopie Pie Recipe!

1 cup of flour

2 tablespoons of sugar

2 tablespoons of baking powder

1 teaspoon of salt

1 egg, beaten

1 cup of buttermilk

2 tablespoons of melted margarine

Step 1   Mix all the dry ingredients together.

Step 2   Next, add the wet ingredients. Stir in the milk, margarine and egg.

Step 3   Whisk the mixture.

Step 4   Use a non-stick frying pan and coat it with a light layer of oil.

Step 5   Use one ladle of batter and spread it over the pan.

Step 6   Cook until the side turns golden brown. Remove the pancake from the pan.

Step 7   Take two pieces of cooked pancakes and sandwich them with either peanut butter or buttercream and jam. Enjoy!

KNOCK KNOCK, GUESS WHO?

It was such an exciting day! First, the chicken escaped from the cage. Everest had figured out how to release the catch on the door. When he opened it, the chicken **FLEW** out! Yes, it can fly!

After Grandpa managed to catch the chicken and put it back in the cage, a policeman came. They said a neighbour had reported screeching and strangling noises coming from our flat. He came to check if we were ill-treating our pet.

When the policeman came into the flat, he shrieked louder than the chicken! I thought it was funny that he was scared of the bird. He said it was illegal to keep a chicken without a permit from the AVA. Whatever that means.

Grandpa lied that the chicken was kept for Amos' science project. Good thing he wasn't home from school yet. He would have protested about the lie!

Grandpa was upset when the policeman took away the chicken. He shut himself up in his room. He said he was becoming a vegetarian for the rest of his life.

How dramatic! I know the policeman is going to release the bird back into the wild. It's free! It can go back to crossing roads. **SQUAWK!**

This evening, Dad helped me borrow a book from the library called "Twelve Steps to Train a Dog!" He asked why I was interested in it. I told him it was for a school project. The book was really disappointing!

There was **NOTHING** about training a poodle to sing, dance and jump through a hoop. Guess I have to make up my own training manual.

How to Train a Poodle

Step 1   Poodle must believe she is really one.
(I can try hypnotising her.)

Step 2   Poodle must learn to sing and dance.
(This is easy, but on her own, she can only
sing The Wonder Girls' Nobody Nobody
But You.)

Step 3   Poodle must learn to jump through a hoop.
(She can twirl the hula hoop around
her waist.)

Step 4   Poodle must look like one.
(I can pleat her long hair and add
pink ribbons.)

Step 5   Poodle must start wearing a collar.
(I must find one.)

That's it! In five easy steps! Me, WHOOPIE LEE,
a genius trainer of the world's first human poodle!

CROCODILES AND POOP ART

Imagine this, you can't find anything about training a human poodle on the Internet, but there are guides on how you can put a crocodile to sleep. This is so amazing…

How to Hypnotise a Crocodile

Step 1   Sneak up on the crocodile from behind.

Step 2   Stand over the crocodile's back with one
          foot on either side of it.

Step 3   Grab the crocodile's head with both
          hands, remember to clamp down hard
          on its jaws.
          If you fail to do this, it's bye-bye for you.

Step 4   Now for the hard part, use all your
          strength and flip the crocodile over so
          that it ends up on its back.

Step 5   Press your hand against the underside
          of the crocodile's mouth and chant three
          times, "You will submit!"

Step 6   If you have done everything right
          so far, your crocodile will fall into
          a dream-like state.

Step 7   Now you can do anything you like with it.
          Paint it pink, purple or add a bow tie
          to its neck. Have fun!

Getting back to school work... here's one more poster
for the Happy Toilet project.

Poop Art

Children living in Szechuan, a province in China, have created an artwork using panda dung (yes, poop!).

They did it with the help of a famous Chinese sculptor, creating a model of Venus de Milo. Venus is a Greek goddess of love and beauty. The original Venus de Milo statue was carved from marble.

The idea of using panda dung for art is not new. Poop offers many uses when it has been treated and baked. In ancient times, people used poop

as "bricks" to build homes. Poop can also be turned into fertiliser for plants and crops.

The dung-based Venus de Milo statue was actually sold to an art collector for a large sum of money! The statue was placed at an art museum, and it became the main draw of attraction. Everyone wanted to see and smell it!

Thumbs up to the children who first came up with the idea.

Wow, a kid in school actually asked me to autograph her copy of the poster! I'm really famous now. The Happy Toilet teacher-in-charge gave me five out of five stars this time. I'm so happy.

Mum posted my poster on her blog too. Yay!

a TOUGH DaY

WEEK 10

I saw Morticia in school. She had a panic attack. She said she didn't want to be a poodle anymore. She had read that dogs can only live up to an average of twelve years. She said, "It's too short a life!" Sometimes I wonder why she's my best friend. I explained to her that it's only a make-believe part. She's not really a poodle.

SHE'S TAKING HER ACTING WAY TOO SERIOUSLY!

She even asked if I could let her be a parrot instead. She found out that the Amazon parrot can live up to eighty years. I told her maybe a land tortoise might be cuter, it can live up to two hundred years!

That shut her up. See, a tortoise isn't cool, right? Never question the playwright.

Then when I got home, Everest decided to pester me. He whined and bugged me for a "bisquik". He meant biscuit. With only six teeth in his mouth, he can't say it properly.

I had saved a copy of "How To Hypnotise A Crocodile", so I decided to try it on Everest. Everything went well until I got to Step 4. He was so **FAT** that when I flipped him over onto his back, he came down on the floor with a crash!

He cried so loudly that Amos came running out of his room. He yelled at me and said he was going to tell Mum that I hurt Everest. He's so evil! Always getting me into trouble.

Everest stopped crying after I bribed him with an entire box of biscuits. I tried Step 5 on him, and he fell asleep very quickly. It has been four hours since the experiment and he's still sleeping. I've looked up the Internet, there's nothing on how to wake up the crocodile!

Then finally, Dad turned on Grandma's Chinese opera tape. The awful singing woke him up.

Guess that's the end of my experiment. To think that I was so close in getting him to sleep when I want him to!

No more hypnotising of crocodiles, or Everest, understand?

Yes, Mum.

How to Train a Poodle (Part II)

Morticia has been working really hard. I got quite far with her training!

Step 1	Poodle must believe she is really one. (I gave her a biscuit, and then told her to repeat after me, "I'm proud to be a poodle!" She's really good at following instructions. No need to hypnotise her.)
Step 2	Poodle must learn to sing and dance. (She did a one-minute song and dance skit. She's cool!)
Step 3	Poodle must learn to jump through a hoop, or do a hula hoop dance. (I timed her when she did it. She can do it for five minutes now. Excellent!)
Step 4	Poodle must look like one. (She looks really cute with pleated hair and pink ribbons. Like a real poodle!)
Step 5	Poodle must start wearing a collar.

I told Morticia she deserved more than a biscuit for her hard work, and gave her a present. She loved it!

She said it's cool to start a fashion trend, wearing a leather collar as a neck-piece. I had to save one week's worth of pocket money for the collar! It was so expensive! I thought it was a little too big for her. But she's happy with it.

The pet shop person said it's the right size for a German Shepherd. See, even boys who look after sheep in Germany wear a collar. This is great! My poodle is ready to star in her first play!

It's mean to make Morticia wear the collar! Stop it! A German Shepherd is a DOG!

Really? Why didn't the pet shop person say so? I've wasted my money for nothing!

A Play by Whoopie Lee, the Genius Playwright

(Part III of The Tale of the Headless Chicken)

SCENE THREE

A forest setting. Poodle is alone on stage. She sits with both arms clutched around her middle. Red Fowl's voice is heard off stage.

RED FOWL You monster! Let me out! I will peck at your insides till you spit me out!

(Poodle suddenly jumps up and does a dance. She is trying her best to force out Red Fowl's head from her stomach.)

RED FOWL Stop jumping around!

(Poodle suddenly breaks out into the song, "I will survive!")

POODLE … you think I'd lay down and die? Oh no, not I! I will survive!

RED FOWL LET ME OUT!

(A hula hoop is rolled onto the stage. Poodle suddenly has an idea. She picks up the hula hoop and starts twirling it around her waist. When she's done, she throws up and out falls Red Fowl from her guts.)

POODLE   Eeeiuw!

(Red Fowl drops to the ground and gives a hard peck at Poodle's feet before rolling off stage. A headless chicken comes running on stage.)

HEADLESS   Where's my head, have you seen it?
CHICKEN

(Poodle takes one horrified look at the headless chicken and faints. The headless chicken squawks and runs off stage.)

End of play.

DiSaPPoiNTMENT

I know Amos has been secretly reading my journal! He called me a bad playwright! I don't know what he meant when he said my play has no dramatic question. He called it a "stupid, frivolous play for poodle-head girls". I'll get back at him one day!

I'll show him who's really stupid. Bet he can't even spell the word. He said it as "pee-volous". **LOL!** No wonder he couldn't get into Raffles Institution.

Mum sent my play to the Singapore Book of Records. The organiser confirmed that this is the first play written by a nine-year-old. But the e-mail said that they cannot endorse a play that "promotes violence and a denial of animal rights".

Violent? Really? All Red Fowl does is to get its head chopped off and eaten alive. What's violent about that? It's only a play! They also rejected Mum's request to have my play listed in the Singapore Book of Records. After the rejection, Mum tried sending my play to several production houses in Singapore.

After two days, she got a reply. The letter said: "The play is an excellent attempt for a nine-year-old. However, we have a budget constraint in casting actors as a headless chicken and a poodle. Please approach someone else."

You know, I could teach them a thing or two. It only costs $3.50 to buy a feather duster. There are at least 87 feathers you could pluck to stick on your head and body. It's not expensive to dress an actor as a chicken! And Morticia said she was willing to act for **FREE!** They don't need to make a poodle suit, she already is one!

Chin up, don't give up yet! What's LOL?

LOL – Laughing Out Loud. I will not give up!

✦ FROM THE DICTIONARY
Frivolous: *[friv-uh-luhs]*
Silly, unimportant and not serious.

WEEK 13

Life in Singapore

Grandpa showed me an article in the newspapers. Singaporeans, it seems, are really a bunch of record breakers. Just look at the silly things we have notched up a "First" for:

★ **Most Number of People Doing a Frog Jump**
(Does this include like, **FAT** people?)

★ **Most Number of People Being a Human Wheelbarrow** (Why? I'm **ROTFL!**)

⭐ The Fastest Text-er!

A world record for sending an SMS text!
41.40 seconds to send out a 160-character text.
(I think Amos can do better than this. He's always
typing on his iPhone in the toilet. Gross!)

⭐ One with the Biggest Mouth!

A nineteen-year-old managed to squeeze and hold
THREE hamburgers in his mouth! (Isn't that like
a **VERY BIG** mouth?)

So why can't the Singapore Book of Records list me as
the **FIRST** nine-year-old to write a play about a headless
chicken and a human poodle?

And get this, a group of Indian chefs even cooked 1,101
fish heads in a curry to break a record! And they said my
play was violent? I only had one headless chicken running
around. They had 1,101 fish heads swimming in a curry!
That's really **CRUEL!**

These are impressive feats! But er... please don't
ever try to prove you have a big mouth!
What's ROTFL?

Rolling On The Floor Laughing.

WEEK 14

FAME AND VIRTUE

Maybe fame is really getting to Morticia's head. She was called up by a teacher for altering her uniform. Morticia had her mum add lace to her skirt. I thought it was quite pretty, but the teacher told her it's against the school rules. The silly girl! Does she really think no one in school would notice?

I've been caught before by eagle-eyed prefects for pulling my skirt too high above my knees. Being the good girl that I am, I will pull it down below the belt holding my pinafore, as I didn't want to get into trouble.

Last year, I performed with Morticia in a school concert. We had our skirts folded and stapled to make it shorter. We did it because we thought it'd be easier to move around. But someone told Mum! She was really upset when she had to remove all the staples from my skirt.

That was also the straw that broke the camel's back. Mum banned me from singing with Morticia after that. She said I was too young to handle fame from being a star. I was unhappy but I got over it. I'm a genius playwright now. I will find fame one day!

Modesty is a virtue, darling! The right length of your skirt should touch the knees.

Yes, Mum.

★ **FROM THE BOOK OF IDIOMS**
The Straw that Broke the Camel's Back
– The last thing that made me lose my fame. I'm **CRBT!**

THE STORY OF THE THREE LITTLE PIGS

Going back to what I know I'm good at, writing plays. How about re-writing a fairy tale? The teachers have talked about it in school. It means taking a fairy tale and telling it differently. Here's my favourite one!

A Fairy Tale by Whoopie Lee, the Genius Playwright

SCENE
A stone house. A pot on a stove. Three little pigs and their Mommy. Baby Pig is sleeping on the floor. Mommy Pig leaves the house and shuts the door behind her.

MOMMY PIG   I'm going to the market!
                      Don't open the door for anyone!

BIG PIG   Yes, Mommy!

(A few minutes pass. Then a wolf knocks on the door pretending to be Mommy Pig.)

WOLF   Kids, I'm home!

BIG PIG   Is that you, Mommy?

MIDDLE PIG   That doesn't sound like Mommy!

BIG PIG   Yes it is, silly!

MIDDLE PIG   Look under the door.
                      See if it's Mommy's feet!

(Big Pig peeps under the door.)

BIG PIG   Mommy, Mommy, your toe nails
                 are HUGE!

(The wolf drops down on his knees quickly.)

WOLF   Oh honey, I forgot to trim my nails.
                 Open now, hurry!

BIG PIG   Yes, Mommy!

MIDDLE PIG   Wait! Tell us the secret password!

BIG PIG   Mommy never told me!

*(Middle Pig pokes Big Pig hard in the ribs. He shrieks
in pain and shuts up.)*

WOLF   Grilled pork chop?

MIDDLE PIG   No!

WOLF   Steamed pork dumpling?

MIDDLE PIG   No!

| WOLF | I know! I know! It's honey-baked pork ribs! |

| MIDDLE PIG | NO! |

| MIDDLE PIG | We can't find the key. Why don't you come in from the chimney? |

| BIG PIG | But the pot is cooking! |

(Middle Pig clobbers Big Pig in the head. He shrieks in pain and shuts up.)

| WOLF | Coming, honey! |

(The wolf takes a ladder and climbs up to the top of the house. He squeezes himself into the chimney and falls through it. He lands in the pot.)

| WOLF | HELP! THE WATER IS BOILING! |

(Big Pig and Middle Pig hear the door opening. Mommy Pig has come home.)

MIDDLE PIG   Mommy! Look!

We trapped the big bad wolf!

(Mommy runs over to the pot and covers it quickly with a lid.)

WOLF   Arrrgghhh!

(Mommy pats Big Pig and Middle Pig on their heads.)

MOMMY PIG   I'm so proud of you!

BIG PIG   So what's the password?

(Baby Pig wakes up from his nap.)

BABY PIG   Bisquik!

End of play.

Desperate measures

Morticia and I surfed the Internet and found a list of people who became famous because they tried eating strange foods. We've narrowed our choice of three yucky foods to eat in our quest for fame:

1   Deep-fried Dragonflies

2   Garlic-roasted Locusts

3   Herbal Cockroach Soup

But Morticia said she felt sick thinking about the horrid foods. I told her that we can shut our eyes and stuff our noses when we have to do it.

Then Mum had to spoil it all, she overheard us talking about it and she yelled, "Who do you think is going to cook these for you!" I had to think before suggesting, "Grandpa!" She said it was "totally disgusting".

That's the first time I've heard her say, "totally".

She's beginning to sound like Amos, so bossy!
Looks like I'm doomed to a life of being a **NOBODY!**

What's worse, Amos complained to Mum that I made him look really "poodle-brained". I know he has read my play. Maybe he's not that dumb, if he can figure out he's one of the pigs.

WEEK
17

WHAT BOYS CAN DO, GIRLS CAN DO TOO!

Morticia found something really interesting on the Internet. It was a model for a paper boat that allows girls to stand while peeing. **AWESOME!**

Morticia printed a copy of the model and had it pasted on cardboard. She did one for me, too. We both tried it privately. It took a while to get it right, but it was easy after some practice.

The paper boat is made in such a way that it allows girls to stand while peeing; the urine falls in and flows out through a little snip at the end of it. It says on the Internet that the paper boat is good for "urgent situations" where toilets, or bushes, can't be found.

This is great! I think Morticia has found the answer to breaking a record! She said all I need to do now is find 1,101 girls to stand and pee together!

Just what are both of you trying to prove? You can't find fame this way!

This is totally INAPPROPRIATE BEHAVIOUR for girls!

What RUBBISH are you reading on the Internet?

Please don't be angry! I'll tell Morticia this is a really **BAD IDEA!** I'm so sorry, Mum! Really, I am!

FiNALLY, FAME!

Something exciting! Mum got a call from a professor teaching at a film school. Here, in Singapore! She said she saw Mum's posting call for actors on Yahoo!

She was interested to audition the playwright and the poodle-girl for a film she's producing. This is so cool! But the best part is that Mum was so pleased that she forgot all about Morticia's **BAD IDEA** to get girls to pee like boys. Phew!

I still can't believe I'm going to be **FAMOUS!** I'm so happy I'm going to be a film star! Mum promised to drive Morticia and me to the audition.

She said it's a prestigious film school that has produced many, many famous Hollywood directors, screenwriters and Oscar-winning actors. I can't believe I'm getting to meet famous people! I'm only nine! What did I do to deserve this? **I'M OVER THE MOON!**

CURTAIN CALL

The audition was one of the longest days of my life. After three hours of waiting for many nine and ten-year-olds to audition, we finally got our turn. Morticia went first. She was really good.

The professor who called Mum asked Morticia to act out a scene from Red Fowl. Morticia acted out Scene Three and did her song, dance and hula hoop twirl beautifully. Then the professor ordered her to show different emotions, like try "happy", "sad", "surprised", "disgusted" and "horrified". She finished her audition in twenty minutes.

Next, it was my turn. There, in the centre of the stage with eighty girls looking, the professor passed me a broomstick! I was so surprised I stared blankly at her.

She asked me to use the broomstick as an acting prop. I panicked and turned to look for Morticia. But I couldn't see her. Mum wasn't allowed in the room either. I was all alone! And **TERRIFIED!**

Finally, I jumped onto the broomstick. I spread one leg on each side and yelled, "Quidditch!" at the top of my lungs. Everyone laughed and cheered for me! Then I pretended I was sweeping the floor with the broom; I tried other things with it, like, weight-lifting and kung fu fighting.

But after that, I had no more ideas. I just couldn't think of anything else! I saw eighty girls staring and waiting. It was horrible! I felt my chin wobble, my shoulders started quaking, and then my knees gave way. I dropped to the floor and couldn't stop my tears. I broke down and cried for Mum.

The professor ran over immediately and wrapped her arms around me. She hushed me and asked, "Is this your 'sad'?"

I cried even louder when I heard that. I was so humiliated! The professor finally realised that I couldn't go on. She thanked me for my effort and told me to leave. I left the room and found Mum and Morticia waiting outside.
I told them I wanted to go home.

I didn't tell Morticia what happened. But Mum knew.

She saw my face and hugged me tight. She said, "You did your best." This is it. My journey for fame has ended. I can never face another crowd for the rest of my life.

Cheer up darling, you did well! I thought 'Quidditch' was brilliant! Focus on your writing; it'll take you far one day!

Love you, Mum.

People you care about

Everest has been really sweet to me. He must have sensed that I was sad. He tried feeding me one of his biscuits this morning. It was grimy from his saliva but I ate it anyway. I didn't want to hurt his feelings.

He snuggled up beside me when I took a nap. He can be a darling. But what got me really surprised was when Amos bought me a bar of Kit Kat. He even wrote a note with it, "Have a break, life still goes on." He stole that line of course, but I thanked him anyway.

As for Morticia, I only have this to say. Looks like fame isn't something you find. You have to earn it. Mum has heard from the professor. Just as I had expected, I didn't get selected. Morticia got in, however. She's being cast in a film that's going to be directed by Oliver Stone (who?). I'm really proud of her!

This afternoon, Morticia came over with a present for me. She made a special card to thank me for helping her get into acting. Awww, it was nothing… she deserves her fame! She worked really hard training for her role.

Mum said that acting will help Morticia to be more confident. Who knows, she might even be a famous movie star one day! But that's a long way to go.

As for me, I've decided that I will stick to writing. To be a genius playwright is something that I can work towards, but, before I become famous, there is something that I need to do.

Morticia and I have decided to make a bid to enter the Singapore Book of Records. We're doing a feat with the hula hoop. It seems that the last person to make it into the Singapore Book of Records did a hula hoop twirl of 169 rounds in one minute. Morticia said she can do better than that. That's the right spirit, girl!

I've included Morticia's card here. See, it's so pretty! It even has a pair of identical friendship bands attached. This is **AWESOME!**

CERTIFICATE

✦ OF AWARD ✦

for

Whoopie Lee

World's Best Trainer
(and Playwright)

Your Best Friend, Morticia Phui
(World's First Human Poodle)

WEEK
21

encore!

One day when I'm famous, people will read this book and remember that I taught them how to put up a play.

How to Stage a Play

Step 1	Write a script.
	(Adapt from a fairy tale if you
	have no ideas.)
Step 2	Find a venue.
	(The living room would do!)
Step 3	Find actors.
	(Ask family members and your best friend.)
Step 4	Make costumes.
	(Use props you can find at home,
	like the feather duster.)
Step 5	Rehearse.
	(Use biscuits to reward hard work,
	but only Mrs. Field's cookies, please.)
Step 6	Stage the play.
	(Invite anyone else not acting to watch,
	if none, set up your stuffed toys as
	the audience.)
Step 7	Buy a bouquet of flowers to present
	to the playwright.
	(Forget the lead actor!)

CREDIT MENTION

Executive Producer	Dad (Because he will pay for the bouquet of flowers.)
Director	Mum (Who else?)
Playwright	Me (A genius!)

CAST FOR THE TALE OF THE HEADLESS CHICKEN & A PUPPY

Old Man	Grandpa
Old Woman	Grandma
Puppy	Morticia
Earthworm	Everest
Red Fowl	Amos

glossary

4D
A four-digit lottery game.

Addams Family
A fictional family in the cartoon series
of the same name.

AVA
Agri-Food & Veterinary Authority
of Singapore.

Kampong

Malay word for "village".

PSLE

Primary School Leaving Examination.

Quidditch

A fictional sport in the Harry Potter series.

Toto

A lottery game.

aBOUT THe auTHor

Adeline Foo, the best-selling author of The Diary of Amos Lee, is a graduate of New York University Tisch School of the Arts Asia. She lives in Singapore with her husband and three children.

Adeline is yet to get listed in the Singapore Book of Records. The closest she got was when she talked her mother, who is sixty-eight years old, into twirling the hula hoop for an hour! But as there were no other witnesses to support the claim, the feat wasn't accepted.

Meanwhile, if you have an idea for an incredible feat that will get you listed in the Singapore Book of Records, do write to her. You can reach her through her website *www.amoslee.com.sg*. Please include your name, age, and school in your e-mails. Hopefully it's something that no one has thought of, like building The Biggest Whoopie Pie in Singapore.

aBOUT THe iLLUSTraTor

Stephanie is a senior designer at Epigram, an independent publishing house dedicated to producing well designed and thought-provoking books.

For other "adorkable" stuff that Stephanie has done, visit *www.steffatplay.blogspot.com*.